THE
1988 CHARLTON
COIN GUIDE

27TH EDITION

Dealer's Buying Prices For
Canadian, Newfoundland and Maritime Coinage
Canadian Medals, Tokens and Paper Money
United States and World Gold Coinage

W. K. Cross
Publisher

(c) Copyright 1988 Charlton International Inc.
All Rights Reserved

ISSN 0706-0459
ISBN 0-88968-064-7

The Charlton Press

15 Birch Avenue, Toronto
Canada M4V 1E1

CONTENTS

While every care has been taken to ensure accuracy in the compilation of the data in this guide, the publisher cannot accept responsibility for typographical errors.

INTRODUCTION

It is more difficult to obtain old coins in circulation, much more so than it was ten years ago. For the most part silver no longer circulates since its bullion value now exceeds its face value. Generally speaking, the only pre-1968 coins in circulation are one-cent and five-cent pieces, and these seldom pre-date 1953. Older coins must now be purchased through dealers.

BUYING AND SELLING PRICES

Buying prices are what dealers pay for coins. Selling prices are what dealers charge for coins. Generally, dealers will pay 40% to 60% of their selling price. It should be remembered, all dealers will pay according to their needs. They will pay well for what they need immediately, but for those coins for which there is no demand, even if they have a high retail value, they will offer substantially less.

The prices shown in this book represent averages or estimates of buying prices, and should serve as a guide in negotiating fair prices when buying or selling. Also a clearer idea of what coins are in demand by collectors and dealers can be developed by studying the guide.

Coins should not be mailed for appraisal unless a written response to an inquiry is received from the dealer. If coins are mailed, then they should be sent by registered mail, insured, accompanied by a list of the coins sent, and with a complete return address and return postage.

HANDLING AND CLEANING COINS

Coins should be handled by the edges only. Avoid touching the surfaces. Many collectors have found too late that fingerprints cannot be removed from coins or other metal valuables. Proof and Specimen quality coins must be handled with extra care since their high lustre is very fragile.

Inevitably, the question of whether to clean coins or not will arise. Probably the best course to follow is, when in doubt - don't, until you have contacted an experienced collector or dealer.

The tarnish on silver coins can be removed, but it will not necessarily raise the value. If the tarnish is very thick, then its removal could leave the coin looking much worse.

Nickel coins seldom require cleaning, and only soap and water are safe since nickel is a fairly active metal. Copper and bronze should not be cleaned by anyone who is not knowledgeable in the chemical properties of these metals and their alloys.

Whatever the metal, abrasives must never be used. There are many polishes on the market which are designed for silverware, copper and brass. These must not be used with coins. The results are disastrous

HANDLING AND CLEANING PAPER MONEY

Inexperienced collectors should always use great care when handling notes. Notes should be handled as little as possible, since oil and perspiration from one's skin can damage and devalue a note. Care should be taken to ensure that unfolded or uncreased notes remain so, and that even marginals tears or abrasions are avoided. Under no circumstances should one ever wash or otherwise try to clean a note since it is likely that the note's value will be considerably reduced. The same is true for ironing or pressing. It should be avoided.

MINT MARKS

A mint mark is a letter stamped on a coin to designate the mint that produced the coins.

Canadian decimal coinage issued prior to 1908 was struck at either the Tower Mint, London, in which case it had no mint mark, or at the Heaton Mint in Birmingham. The Birmingham coins had a small "H" as a mint mark. Since 1908 all Canadian coins have been struck at the Ottawa or Winnipeg Mints, with no mint marks, except the Canadian sovereigns which were identified by a small "C" above the date.

Newfoundland's coinage was struck at either London, Birmingham, or Ottawa. The Tower Mint coins had no marks, the Birmingham coins had an "H", and the Ottawa coins had a "C", except for the 1940 and 1942 cent pieces.

New Brunswick's and Nova Scotia's coinage had no mint marks because it was struck at the Tower Mint.

Prince Edward Island's coinage was struck at Birmingham but no mint mark was used because the dies were supplied by the Tower Mint.

NOVA SCOTIA

VICTORIA 1861 - 1864

Date and Denomination	Buying Price
1861 half cent	1.50
1864 half cent	1.50
1861 one cent	.40
1862 one cent	5.00
1864 one cent	.40

NEW BRUNSWICK

VICTORIA 1861 - 1864

Date and Denomination	Buying Price
1861 half cent	16.00
1861 one cent	.40
1864 one cent	.40
1862 five cents	10.00
1864 five cents	10.00
1862 ten cents	9.00
1864 ten cent	9.00
1862 twenty cents	5.00
1864 twenty cents	5.00

PRINCE EDWARD ISLAND

VICTORIA 1871

Date and Denomination	Buying Price
1871 one cent	.30

IMPORTANT

Mint marks are a letter stamped on a coin to designate the Mint that produced the coin. The Canadian Mint used the letter "C", while the Heaton Mint in England used the letter "H".

IMPORTANT

Do not clean your coins. Coins should be handled carefully. Only experts should consider cleaning. If you are not an expert the results can be disastrous

NEWFOUNDLAND

LARGE CENTS

GEORGE V 1913 - 1936

Date and Mint Mark	Description	Buying Price
1913		.10
1917C		.10
1919C		.10
1920C		.10
1929		.10
1936		.10

Round O   Oval O

VICTORIA 1865 - 1896

Date and Mint Mark	Description	Buying Price
1865		.40
1872H		.40
1873		.40
1876H		.40
1880	Round O	.40
1880	Oval O	25.00
1885		4.00
1888		4.00
1890		.40
1894		.40
1896		.40

SMALL CENTS

GEORGE VI 1938 - 1948

Date and Mint Mark	Description	Buying Price
1938		.10
1940		.25
1941C		.03
1942		.03
1943C		.03
1944C		.15
1947C		.05

FIVE CENTS

EDWARD VII 1904 - 1909

Date and Mint Mark	Description	Buying Price
1904H		1.00
1907		.30
1909		.30

VICTORIA 1865 - 1896

Date and Mint Mark	Description	Buying Price
1865		8.0
1870		10.0
1872H		8.0
1873		10.0

Date and Mint Mark	Description	Buying Price
1873H		300.00
1876H		20.00
1880		8.00
1881		4.00
1882H		3.50
1885		40.00
1888		7.00
1890		1.00
1894		1.00
1896		1.00

EDWARD VII 1903 - 1908

Date and Mint Mark	Description	Buying Price
1903		1.00
1904H		.40
1908		.40

GEORGE V 1912 - 1929

Date and Mint Mark	Description	Buying Price
1912		.40
1917C		.40
1919C		.40
1929		.30

GEORGE VI 1938 - 1947

Date and Mint Mark	Description	Buying Price
1938		.20
1940C		.20
1941C		.20
1942C		.20
1943C		.20
1944C		.20
1945C		.20
1946C		100.00
1947C		.20

TEN CENTS

VICTORIA 1865 - 1896

Date and Mint Mark	Description	Buying Price
1865		4.00
1870		65.00
1872H		4.00
1873		5.50
1876H		8.00
1880		8.00
1882H		4.00
1885		20.00
1888		3.50
1890		1.25
1894		1.25
1896		1.00

EDWARD VII 1903 - 1904

Date and Mint Mark	Description	Buying Price
1903		.40
1904H		.40

GEORGE V 1912 - 1919

Date and Mint Mark	Description	Buying Price
1912		.40
1917C		.40
1919C		.40

IMPORTANT

Buying prices are listed for coins graded VG or better. Bent, damaged or badly worn coins are not collectable and bring no premium value.

GEORGE VI 1938 - 1947

Date and Mint Mark	Description	Buying Price
1938		.40
1940		.40
1941C		.40
1942C		.40
1943C		.40
1944C		.40
1945C		.40
1946C		1.00
1947C		.40

EDWARD VII 1904

Date and Mint Mark	Description	Buying Price
1904H		.95

GEORGE V 1912

Date and Mint Mark	Description	Buying Price
1912		.95

TWENTY CENTS

VICTORIA 1865 - 1900

Date and Mint Mark	Description	Buying Price
1865		3.00
1870		4.00
1872H		2.00
1873		3.00
1876H		4.00
1880		5.00
1881		.95
1882H		.95
1885		.95
1888		.95
1890		.95
1894		.95
1896		.95
1899		.95
1900		.95

TWENTY-FIVE CENTS

GEORGE V 1917 - 1919

Date and Mint Mark	Description	Buying Price
1917C		.95
1919C		.95

IMPORTANT

Buying prices are listed for coins graded VG or better. Bent, damaged or badly worn coins are not collectable and bring no premium value.

IMPORTANT

Mint marks are a letter stamped on a coin to designate the mint that produced the coin. The Canadian Mint used the letter "C", while the Heaton Mint in England used the letter "H".

FIFTY CENTS

GEORGE V 1911 - 1919

Date and Mint Mark	Description	Buying Price
1911		1.90
1917C		1.90
1918C		1.90
1919C		1.90

VICTORIA 1870 - 1900

Date and Mint Mark	Description	Buying Price
1870		2.50
1872H		2.50
1873		4.00
1874		2.00
1876H		5.00
1880		6.00
1881		2.50
1882H		2.00
1885		2.50
1888		3.00
1894		2.00
1896		2.00
1898		2.00
1899		1.90
1900		1.90

TWO DOLLARS GOLD

VICTORIA 1865 - 1888

Date and Mint Mark	Description	Buying Price
1865		125.00
1870		125.00
1872		175.00
1880		700.00
1881		110.00
1882H		110.00
1885		110.00
1888		110.00

EDWARD VII 1904 - 1909

Date and Mint Mark	Description	Buying Price
1904H		1.90
1907		1.90
1908		1.90
1909		1.90

PROVINCE OF CANADA

LARGE CENTS

VICTORIA 1858 - 1859

Date and Mint Mark	Description	Buying Price
1858		14.00
1859		.50
1859	W/9 over 8	9.00

FIVE CENTS

Large Date   Small Date

VICTORIA 1858

Date and Mint Mark	Description	Buying Price
1858	Small Date	2.00
1858	Large Date	30.00

IMPORTANT
Mint marks are a letter stamped on a coin to designate the mint that produced the coin. The Canadian Mint used the letter "C", while the Heaton Mint in England used the letter "H".

TEN CENTS

VICTORIA 1858

Date and Mint Mark	Description	Buying Price
1858		2.50

TWENTY CENTS

VICTORIA 1858

Date and Mint Mark	Description	Buying Price
1858		20.00

IMPORTANT
The buying prices for silver coins are based on their intrinsic value. All issues from 1902 to 1968 are priced at the market value for $8.00 (Can. Funds) silver. Conditions play an important part in the buying price for coins between 1902 and 1936. Higher or lower silver prices will change the listed values.

IMPORTANT
Buying prices are listed for coins graded VG or better. Bent, damaged or badly worn coins are not collectable and bring no premium value.

DOMINION OF CANADA

LARGE CENTS

Large Date, Large Leaves

Small Date, Small Leaves

EDWARD VII 1902 -1910

Date and Mint Mark	Description	Buying Price
1902		.25
1903		.25
1904		.25
1905		.25
1906		.25
1907		.25
1907H		2.00
1908		.30
1909		.30
1910		.30

VICTORIA 1876 - 1901

Date and Mint Mark	Description	Buying Price
1876H		.50
1881H		.60
1882H		.50
1884		.50
1886		.60
1887		.50
1888		.50
1890H		.60
1891	Large Date	1.25
1891	Small Date	15.00
1892		.50
1893		.50
1894		.50
1895		.50
1896		.50
1897		.50
1898H		.50
1899		.50
1900		.50
1900H		.50
1901		.50

Large Cents were not issued for the years omitted in this listing.

GEORGE V 1911 - 1920

Date and Mint Mark	Description	Buying Price
1911		.15
1912		.15
1913		.15
1914		.15
1915		.15
1916		.15
1917		.15
1919		.15
1918		.15
1920		.15

IMPORTANT
Buying prices are listed for coins graded VG or better. Bent, damaged or badly worn coins are not collectable and bring no premium value.

SMALL CENTS

GEORGE VII 1920 - 1936

Date and Mint Mark	Description	Buying Price
1920		.03
1921		.03
1922		2.50
1923		6.50
1924		1.00
1925		3.50
1926		.50
1927		.15
1928		.03
1929		.03
1930		.30
1931		.10
1932 to 1936		.03

No Shoulder Fold   Shoulder Fold

ELIZABETH II 1953 to date

Date and Mint Mark	Description	Buying Price
1953	NSF	.01
1953	SF	.05
1954 to 1964		.01

1937 Obverse   1937 Reverse

1947 Maple Leaf

GEORGE VI 1937 - 1952

Date and Mint Mark	Description	Buying Price
1937 to 1947		.01
1947	Maple Leaf	.01

In 1948 "ET IND:IMP." ceased to appear on the coinage.

Date and Mint Mark	Description	Buying Price
1965		.01
1956		.01
1967	Centennial	.01
1968 to 1981		.01

Date and Mint Mark	Description	Buying Price
1948 to 1952		.01

Date and Mint Mark	Description	Buying Price
1982 to 1988		.01

FIVE CENTS SILVER

Small H   Large H

1900 Small Date   1900 Large Date

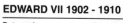

Plain 4   Crosslet 4

VICTORIA 1870 - 1901

Date and Mint Mark	Description	Buying Price
1870		1.50
1871		1.75
1872H		1.25
1874H	Plain 4	3.50
1874H	Crosslet 4	2.00
1875H	Large Date	40.00
1875H	Small Date	30.00
1880H		.80
1881H		1.00
1882H		1.00
1883H		2.00
1884		25.00
1885		1.00
1886		1.00
1887		3.00
1888		.75
1889		4.00
1890H		1.00
1891		.75
1892		1.00
1893		.75
1894		2.50
1896		.75
1897		.75
1898		2.00
1899		.75
1900	Large Date	5.00
1900	Small Date	.75
1901		.75

EDWARD VII 1902 - 1910

Date and Mint Mark	Description	Buying Price
1902	Plain	.40
1902	Large H	.50
1902	Small H	3.00
1903		1.00
1903H		.40
1904		.40
1905		.40
1906		.40
1907		.40
1908		1.00
1909		.40
1910		.30

GEORGE V 1911 - 1921

Date and Mint Mark	Description	Buying Price
1911		.25
1912		.25
1913		.25
1914		.30
1915		2.00
1916		.50
1917		.25
1918		.25
1919		.25
1920		.25
1921		600.00

FIVE CENTS NICKEL

Near 6   Far 6

GEORGE V 1922 - 1936

Date and Mint Mark	Description	Buying Price
1922 to 1924		.06
1925		9.00
1926	Near 6	.25
1926	Far 6	30.00
1927 to 1936		.06

Tombac Beaver

Tombac "V"   1947 Maple Leaf

GEORGE VI 1937 - 1952

Date and Mint Mark	Description	Buying Price
1937	Dot	.05
1938 to 1941		.05
1942	Nickel	.05
1942	Tombac Beaver	.07
1943	Tombac V	.07
1944 to 1945	Steel V	.05
1946 to 1947		.05
1947	Maple Leaf	.05

In 1948 "ET IND:IMP." ceased to appear on the coinage.

1948

Date and Mint Mark	Description	Buying Price
1948 to 1950		.05

1951 Beaver   1951 Commemorative

Date and Mint Mark	Description	Buying Price
1951	Commemorative	.05
1951	Beaver	.05
1952		.05

ELIZABETH II 1953 to date

Date and Mint Mark	Description	Buying Price
1953 to 1966		.05
1967	Centennial	.05
1968 to 1988		.05

TEN CENTS

Flat Top 3	Round Top 3

VICTORIA 1870 - 1901

Date and Mint Mark	Description	Buying Price
1870		2.50
1871		2.50
1871H		3.50
1872H		20.00
1874H		1.25
1875H		60.00
1880H		1.25
1881H		2.50
1882H		1.25
1883H		4.00
1884		40.00
1885		3.00
1886		2.00
1887		4.00
1888		1.00
1889		125.00
1890H		2.00
1891		2.00
1892		1.25
1893	Flat Top 3	2.50
1893	Round Top 3	125.00
1894		.25
1986		1.25
1898		1.25
1899		1.00
1900		.50
1901		.50

EDWARD VII 1902 - 1910

Date and Mint Mark	Description	Buying Price
1902		.45
1902H		.45
1903		.45

Date and Mint Mark	Description	Buying Price
1903H		.45
1904		.45
1905		.45
1906		.45
1907		.45
1908		.45
1909		.45
1910		.45

Small Leaves	Broad Leaves

GEORGE V 1911 - 1936

Date and Mint Mark	Description	Buying Price
1911		1.00
1912		.40
1913	Broad Leaves	25.00
1913	Small Leaves	.40
1914 to 1936		.40

GEORGE VI 1937 - 1952

Date and Mint Mark	Description	Buying Price
1937 to 1947		.40
1947 Maple Leaf		.40

IMPORTANT
Buying prices are listed for coins graded VG or better. Bent, damaged or badly worn coins are not collectable and bring no premium value.

In 1948 "ET IND:IMP." ceased to appear on coinage.

Date and Mint Mark	Description	Buying Price
1948		.80
1949 to 1952		.40

1969 Small Date   1969 Large Date

ELIZABETH II 1953 to date

Date and Mint Mark	Description	Buying Price
1953 to 1966		.40
1967	Centennial	.35
1968	.500 Fine	.25
1968	Nickel	.10
1969	Large Date	2,000.00
1969	Small Date	.10
1970 to 1988	Nickel	.10

TWENTY-FIVE CENTS

Narrow O   Wide O

VICTORIA 1870 - 1901

Date and Mint Mark	Description	Buying Price
1870		2.00
1871		3.00
1871H		3.50
1872H		1.25
1874H		1.25
1875H		75.00
1880H	Narrow 0	8.00
1880	Wide 0	25.00
1881H		2.00
1882H		3.00
1883H		1.50
1885		20.00
1886		2.00
1887		20.00
1888		2.00
1889		25.00
1890H		3.00
1891		10.00
1892		1.50
1893		15.00
1894		.95
1899		.95
1900		.95
1901		.95

IMPORTANT
Do not clean your coins. Coins should be handled carefully. Only experts should consider cleaning. If you are not an expert the results can be disasterous.

EDWARD VII 1902 - 1910

Date and Mint Mark	Description	Buying Price
1902		.95
1902H		.95
1903		.95
1904		.95
1905		.95
1906		.95
1907		.95
1908		.95
1909		.95
1910		.95

GEORGE V 1911 - 1936

Date and Mint Mark	Description	Buying Price
1911		2.00
1912 to 1914		.95
1915		3.00
1916 to 1920		.95
1921		2.00
1927		4.00
1928 to 1936		.95
1936	Dot	10.00

GEORGE VI 1937 - 1952

Date and Mint Mark	Description	Buying Price
1937 to 1947		.95
1947	Maple Leaf	.95

In 1948 "ET IND:IMP." ceased to appear on the coinage.

Date and Mint Mark	Description	Buying Price
1948 to 1952		.95

Obverse
1953-64

Obverse
1965-88

ELIZABETH II 1953 to date

Date and Mint Mark	Description	Buying Price
1953	Large Date	.95
1953	Small Date	.95
1954 to 1966		.95
1967	Centennial	.75
1968	.500 Fine	.50
1968 to 1972	Nickel	.25

IMPORTANT
Do not clean your coins. Coins should be handled carefully. Only experts should consider cleaning. If you are not an expert the results can be disasterous.

Large Bust
132 Obverse Beads

Small Bust
120 Obverse Beads

Date and Mint Mark	Description	Buying Price
1973	Small Bust	.25
1973	Large Bust	75.00
1974 to 1988	Nickel	.25

FIFTY CENTS

L.C.W.   No L.C.W.

VICTORIA 1870 - 1901

Date and Mint Mark	Description	Buying Price
1870	Without L.C.W.	200.00
1870	With L.C.W.	8.00
1871		12.00
1871H		20.00
1872H		10.00

1881H	9.00
1888	40.00
1890H	300.00
1892	15.00
1894	75.00
1898	12.00
1899	20.00
1900	8.00
1901	8.00

EDWARD VII 1902 - 1910

Date and Mint Mark	Description	Buying Price
1902		3.00
1903H		4.00
1904		25.00
1905		30.00
1906		1.90
1907		1.90
1908		1.90
1909		1.90
1910		1.90

GEORGE V 1911 - 1936

Date and Mint Mark	Description	Buying Price
1911 to 1920		1.9
1921*		3,000.0
1929		1.9
1931		1.9
1932		12.0
1934		3.0
1936		2.0

*Majority were melted down, approximate
75 are known. Beware of altered date.

Maple Leaf   No Maple Leaf

1947 Straight "7"

Maple Leaf   No Maple Leaf

1947 Curved "7"

GEORGE VI 1937 - 1952

Date and Mint Mark	Description	Buying Price
1937 to 1946		1.90
1947	Straight 7"	1.90
1947	Curved 7"	1.90
1947	M.L., Straight 7"	5.00
1947	M.L., Curved 7"	600.00

n 1948 "ET IND:IMP." ceased to appear on he coinage.

Date and Mint Mark	Description	Buying Price
948		15.00
949 to 1952		1.90

No Shoulder Fold   Shoulder Fold

Small Date   Large Date

ELIZABETH II 1953 to date

Date and Mint Mark	Description	Buying Price
1953	SD,NSF	1.90
1953	LD,NSF	2.50
1953	LD,SF	1.90
1954 to 1964		1.90

Date and Mint Mark	Description	Buying Price
1965 to 1966		1.90
1967	Centennial	1.90
1968 to 1988	Nickel	.50

17

SILVER DOLLARS

1935 Obverse

1936 Obverse

1937 Obverse

1935 Reverse

1939 Parliament

1949 Newfoundland

1947 Blunt 7   1947 Pointed 7

1947 Maple Leaf

1952
Waterlines

1952
No Waterlines

GEORGE V 1935 - 1936

Date and Mint Mark	Description	Buying Price
1935	Silver Jubilee	7.00
1936	Voyageur	7.00

GEORGE VI 1937 - 1952

Date and Mint Mark	Description	Buying Price
1937	Voyageur	7.00
1938	Voyageur	12.00
1939	Royal Visit	5.00
1945	Voyageur	50.00
1946	Voyageur	12.00
1947	Blunt 7	20.00

Date and Mint Mark	Description	Buying Price
1947	Pointed 7	60.00
1947	Maple Leaf	75.00
1948	Dei Gratia	350.00
1949	Newfoundland	7.00
1950	Voyageur	5.00
1950	Arnprior	6.00
1951	Voyageur	5.00
1951	Arnprior	20.00
1952	Waterlines	5.00
1952	No Waterlines	5.00

Arnprior dollars are known to exist in the years 1950, 1951 and 1955. Other years may contain Arnpriors but are not known to exist

| Obverse | 1953 | Reverse | 1964 Charlottetown |

| 1958 British Columbia | 1965 Obverse | 1967 Centennial |

1955 No Water Lines   1955 1 1/2 Waterlines

ELIZABETH II 1953 to date

Date and Mint Mark	Description	Buying Price	Date and Mint Mark	Description	Buying Price
1953	Voyageur	4.00	1960	Voyageur	4.00
1954	Voyageur	4.00	1961	Voyageur	4.00
1955	Voyageur	4.00	1962	Voyageur	4.00
1955	Arnprior	40.00	1963	Voyageur	4.00
1956	Voyageur	4.00	1964	Charlottetown	4.00
1957	Voyageur	4.00	1965	Voyageur	4.00
1957	One Waterline	4.00	1966	Voyageur	4.00
1958	British Columbia	4.00	1967	Centennial	4.00
1959	Voyageur	4.00			

IMPORTANT

Do not clean your coins. Coins should be handled carefully. Only experts should consider cleaning. If you are not an expert the results can be disasterous.

NICKEL DOLLARS

Manitoba

British Columbia

Prince Edward Island

Winnipeg

Constitution

Jacques Cartier

1968 Obverse

Obverse

Loon

Reverse

Date and Mint Mark	Description	Buying Price	Date and Mint Mark	Description	Buying Price
1968	Voyageur	1.00	1982	Constitution	1.00
1969	Voyageur	1.00	1983	Voyageur	1.00
1970	Manitoba	1.00	1984	Jacques Cartier	1.00
1971	British Columbia	1.00	1985	Voyageur	1.00
1972	Voyageur	1.00	1986	Voyageur	1.00
1973	P.E.I.	1.00	1987	Voyageur	1.00
1974	Winnipeg	1.00	1987	Loon	1.00
1975 to 1981	Voyageur	1.00	1988	Loon	1.00

GOLD COINS

SOVEREIGNS

EDWARD VII 1908 - 1910

Date and Mint Mark	Description	Buying Price
1908C		900.00
1909C		150.00
1910C		150.00

GEORGE V 1911 - 1919

Date and Mint Mark	Description	Buying Price
1911C		150.00
1913C		275.00
1914C		150.00
1916C		6,000.00
1917C		150.00
1918C		150.00
1919C		150.00

FIVE DOLLARS

GEORGE V 1912 - 1914

Date and Mint Mark	Description	Buying Price
1912		150.00
1913		150.00
1914		250.00

TEN DOLLARS

GEORGE V 1912 - 1914

Date and Mint Mark	Description	Buying Price
1912		310.00
1913		310.00
1914		350.00

TWENTY DOLLARS

ELIZABETH II 1953 -

Date and Mint Mark	Description	Buying Price
1967	Centennial	300.00
1967	Complete Set	305.00

IMPORTANT
Do not clean your coins. Coins should be handled carefully. Only experts should consider cleaning. If you are not an expert the results can be disasterous.

ONE HUNDRED DOLLARS

The first issue of one hundred dollar gold coins began in 1976 and has been continued to date. Each coin with the exception of the 1976 an d 1987 14 kt issues contain one half an ounce of gold, the 1976 and 1987 14 kt coins contain a quarter ounce. All but the 1976 14 kt coin were issued in proof condition, the highest quality the Royal Canadian Mint produces. All gold coins have the common obverse portrait of Queen Elizabeth.

1976 - 14 kt   1976 - 22 kt

1977 1978 1979 1980

1981 1982 1983 1984

1985 1986 1987 - 14 kt

Date	Description	Buying Price	Date	Description	Buying Price
1976	14 kt Olympic	118.00	1982	Constitution	235.00
1976	22 kt Olympic	235.00	1983	Gilbert's Landing	235.00
1977	Jubilee	250.00	1984	Voyage of Discovery	275.00
1978	Unity	235.00	1985	National Parks	275.00
1979	Year of the Child	235.00	1986	Peace	275.00
1980	Arctic Territories	240.00	1987	Winter Olympic Games	275.00
1981	"O" Canada	250.00			

ONE HUNDRED DOLLARS
IMPORTANT

Proof gold coins must be in mint state condition. Mishandled, mounted or damaged coins are discounted from the prices listed. The buying price for gold coins is tied to the market price of gold. Any movement on the gold price will result in a corresponding price movement in these coins.

MAPLE LEAF BULLION GOLD COINS

The Maple Leaf gold coins were first produced in 1979, the fractional or small sizes three years later in 1982 and the half ounce size in 1986.

| $50 | $20 | $10 | $5 |

The four sizes of Maple Leaf gold coins are purchased based on the spot gold market price on the day of sale times their gold content less a small handling charge.

GOLD CONTENTS

| 1/10 Maple Leaf | $5 – 0.10 Troy ounce | 1/2 Maple Leaf | $20 – 0.50 Troy ounce |
| 1/4 Maple Leaf | $10 – 0.25 Troy ounce | Maple Leaf | $50 – 1.00 Troy ounce |

COLLECTORS ISSUES

The Numismatic department of the Royal Canadian Mint issued specially struck and packaged coins starting in 1954. The coins were issued for collectors and as a result are of high quality. The dealer buying prices listed below are for single coins and sets in their original packaging and condition. Coins or sets which have been mishandled or damaged are discounted from the prices listed. Beginning in 1981 the Numismatic Department of the Royal Canadian Mint issued silver dollars for collectors in two conditions, proof and uncirculated. Proof condition dollars were issued in black leatherette boxes and uncirculated dollars were issued in a clear plastic container.

SILVER PROOF-LIKE DOLLAR

Date	Description	Buying Price
1954	Voyageur	90.00
1955	Voyageur	75.00
1955	Arnprior	110.00
1956	Voyageur	45.00
1957	Voyageur	18.00
1958	British Columbia	12.00
1959	Voyageur	8.00
1960	Voyageur	6.00
1961	Voyageur	6.00
1962	Voyageur	5.00
1963	Voyageur	5.00
1964	Charlottetown	5.00

CASED NICKEL DOLLARS

Date	Description	Buying Price
1968 to 1976	Voyageur	1.00
1982	Constitution	3.00
1984	Jacques Cartier	3.00
1985 to 1986	Voyageur	1.00
1987	Loon	5.00

CASED SILVER DOLLARS

Date	Description	Buying Price
1971	British Columbia	4.00
1972	Voyageur	5.00
1973	R.C.M.P.	3.50
1974	Winnipeg	3.50
1975	Calgary Stampede	3.50
1976	Library of Parliament	4.50
1977	Jubilee	3.50
1978	Commonwealth Games	3.50
1979	Griffon	5.00
1980	Arctic Territories	10.00
1981	Trans Canada (PF)	25.00
1981	Trans Canada (UNC)	6.00
1982	Regina (PF)	10.00
1982	Regina (UNC)	6.00
1983	University Games (PF)	10.00
1983	University Games (UNC)	6.00
1984	Toronto (PF)	10.00
1984	Toronto (UNC)	6.00
1985	National Parks (PF)	10.00
1985	National Parks (UNC)	6.00
1986	Vancouver (PF)	10.00
1986	Vancouver (UNC)	6.00
1987	Davis Strait (PF)	10.00
1987	Davis Strait (UNC)	6.00
1988	(PF)	10.00
1988	(UNC)	6.00

SILVER PROOF-LIKE SETS

Date	Description	Buying Price
1954	Voyageur	200.00
1955	Voyageur	100.00
1955	Arnprior	150.00
1956	Voyageur	60.00
1957	Voyageur	30.00
1958	British Columbia	20.00
1959	Voyageur	12.00
1960	Voyageur	9.00
1961	Voyageur	9.00
1962	Voyageur	9.00
1963	Voyageur	9.00
1964	Charlottetown	9.00
1965	Voyageur	9.00
1966	Voyageur	9.00
1967	Centennial	9.00

NICKEL PROOF-LIKE SETS

Date	Description	Buying Price
1968	Voyageur	2.0
1969	Voyageur	2.0
1970	Manitoba	2.0
1971	British Columbia	2.0
1972	Voyageur	2.0
1973	R.C.M.P.Small Bust	2.0
1973	R.C.M.P.Large Bust	50.0
1974	Winnipeg	2.0
1975	Voyageur	2.0
1976	Voyageur	2.0
1977	Voyageur	2.0
1978	Voyageur	2.0
1979	Voyageur	2.5
1980	Voyageur	5.0
1981	Voyageur	3.0
1982	Voyageur	2.5
1983	Voyageur	2.5
1984	Voyageur	3.0
1985	Voyageur	3.0
1986	Voyageur	3.0
1987	Voyageur	3.
1988	Loon	3.

CUSTOM SETS

Issued by the Royal Canadian Mint between 1971 and 1981, contains 1-cent to the nickel dollar plus an extra cent (7 coins).

Date	Description	Buying Price
1971 to 1981		2.0

SPECIMEN SETS

Issued by the Royal Mint starting in 1981 and continuing to date, contains the 1-cent to the nickel dollar (6 coins).

Date	Description	Buying Price
1981		4.
1982		4.
1983		4.
1984		4.
1985		4.
1986		4.
1987		4.
1988		4.

PRESTIGE PROOF SETS

Issued by the Royal Canadian Mint starting in 1971 and continuing to date, contains the 1-cent to the nickel dollars plus the silver dollar of that year (7 coins).

SPECIMEN SETS

Sets of Specimen coins have been issued in Canada at various times since 1858, often in official cases. A representative selection follows. Sets from 1908 are in leather or leatherette covered presentation cases.

Date	Description	Buying Price	Date	Description	Buying Price
1971		7.00	1858	Victoria:	
1972		15.00		1 ,5, 10, 20-cents	1,500.00
1973		6.00	1870	Victoria:	
1974		6.00		5, 10, 25, 50-cents	3,000.00
1975		6.00	1908	Edward VII:	
1976		7.00		1, 5, 10, 25, 50-cents	500.00
1977		6.00	1911	George V:	
1978		6.00		1, 5, 10,25, 50-cents	2,000.00
1979		7.00	1937	George VI:	
1980		12.00		1, 5, 10, 25, 50-cents $1	400.00
1981		30.00	1937	George VI	
1982		11.00		as above, but in card case	300.00
1983		12.00	1967	Elizabeth II: Centennial,	
1984		15.00		1, 5, 10, 25, 50 cents	
1985		15.00		$1.00, $20,00 gold	305.00
1986		15.00	1967	Elizabeth II: Centennial,	
1987		15.00		as above, but with medal	
1988		15.00		instead of 20.00 gold	$15.00

1976 MONTREAL OLYMPIC COINS

For the Summer Olympic Games of 1976, held in Montreal, seven series of silver coins were minted. There were four different coins in each series. Two $5 and two $10 coins, struck in sterling silver. The $5 coins weigh 24.3 grams and the $10 coins weigh 48.6 grams. The coins were available, encapsulated in plastic as single coins, and in Custom, Prestige and Proof for coin sets. Each set of four coins, $30.00, contains 4.28 oz of fine silver. The purchase price of these sets is linked to the market price of silver.

SERIES I 1973

$ 5 Map of North America
$ 5 Kingston
$10 World Map
$10 Montreal

SERIES II 1974

$ 5 Athlete with Torch
$ 5 Olive Wreath
$10 Head of Zeus
$10 Temple of Zeus

SERIES III 1974

$ 5 Canoeing
$ 5 Rowing
$10 Lacrosse
$10 Bicycling

SERIES IV 1975

$ 5 The Marathon
$ 5 Ladies' Javelin
$10 Men's Hurdles
$10 Ladies' Shot Put

SERIES V 1975

$ 5 The Diver
$ 5 The Swimmer
$10 The Paddler
$10 Sailing

SERIES VI 1976

$ 5 Fencing
$ 5 Boxing
$10 Field Hockey
$10 Football

SERIES VII 1976

$ 5 Olympic Village
$ 5 Olympic Flame
$10 Olympic Stadium
$10 Olympic Velodrome

Buying Price:		
Single $ 5		5.25
Single $10		10.50
Four Coin Custom and Prestige Sets		32.00
Four Coin Proof Set		35.00

1988 CALGARY OLYMPIC GAMES

The XV Winter Olympic Games will be held in Calgary, February 13th to 29th, 1988. Ten different $20 silver coins were issued to commemorate this event. The coins weigh 34.107 grams, the composition is .925 silver and .075 copper, and the coins were issued in Proof-singles or Proof-Sets in one or two coin display cases. Incorporated into the design of these coins are the letters "XV OLYMPIC WINTER GAMES - XV es JEUX OLYMPIQUE D'HIVER" impressed into the edge. During the striking of these coins at the Royal Canadian Mint the impressed procedures were skipped on some series resulting in the edge lettering being missed on four known coins resulting in varieties.

SERIES I 1985		SERIES IV 1987	
Downhill Skiing	25.00	Figure Skating	25.00
Speed Skating	25.00	Curling	25.00
Speed Skating, no edge lettering	50.00		

SERIES II 1986		SERIES V 1987	
		Ski-Jumping	25.00
Hockey	25.00	Bobsleigh	25.00
Hockey, no edge lettering	50.00		
Biathalon	25.00		
Biathalon, no edge lettering	50.00		

SERIES III 1986

Cross-Country Skiing	25.00
Free-Style Skiing	25.00
Free-Style Skiing, no edge lettering	50.00

COLONIAL COINS AND TOKENS

Canada has produced a great number of tokens of various kings over the years. Tokens were used as a form of currency prior to the institution of the decimal currency system in 1858 Colonial issues are not all tokens, some being regal coins). After Confederation, other kinds f tokens appeared, such as those for services, transportation and advertising purposes.

The prices in this section are for tokens in V.G. (Very Good) or F. (Fine) condition. Higher rices will be paid for rare issues or for tokens in V.F. (Very Fine) or better condition.

FRENCH REGIME

Sol 1738-1754   Buy Price - $2.00

NOVA SCOTIA

Date and Description	Buying Price
1824-1856 Penny	.75
1823-1856 Halfpenny	.50
White's Farthing	5.00

NEW BRUNSWICK

27

Date and Description	Buying Price
1840 Plough	.4
1840 Sheaf of Wheat	50.0
1855 Self-Government	.
1858 Ship	.

Date and Description	Buying Price
1830 St. John Halfpenny	3.00
1834-1854 Penny	.50
1843-1854 Penny	.60

PRINCE EDWARD ISLAND

NEWFOUNDLAND

Date and Description		Buying Price
1846	Rutherford Halfpenny	
Ship		75.

LOWER CANADA

Date and Description	Buying Price
1815 Magdalen Island Penny	3.50
1824 Owen's Ropery	300.00
1837 Molson's Halfpenny	15.00
1838-1839 Bank of Montreal	
Sideview Halfpenny	45.00
Sideview Penny	100.00

Date and Description	Buying Price
1822 Lesslie Twopence	20.00
1816 Isaac Brock	.50
1832 Halfpenny	2.00

PROVINCE OF UPPER CANADA

PROVINCE OF CANADA

BRITISH COLUMBIA

Date and Description	Buying Price
1802 Pattern Gold $10	Very Rare
1802 Pattern Gold $20	Very Rare

NORTH WEST COMPANY

Date and Description	Buying Price
1820 North West Company Token	100.0

HUDSON'S BAY COMPANY

Set of Four Tokens

Date and Description	Buying Price
1842-1844 Bank of Montreal	
Frontview Halfpenny	.25
1837 Front View Penny	35.00
1842 Front View Penny	.75
1852 Quebec Bank Penny	.50
Halfpenny	.30
1850-1857 Bank of Upper Canada	
Halfpenny	.20
Penny	.30
Copper Company of Canada	
Halfpenny (Proof)	75.00

Date and Description	Buying Price
Bridge Tokens	40.00
Montreal & Lachine Railroad Tokens	20.00

Date and Description	Buying Price
Hudson's Bay Company Tokens Set of four (1,1/2,1/4,1/8)	30.00

TRANSPORTATION TOKENS

ADVERTISING PIECES

Date and Description	Buying Price
Purves	1.50
Blackley	1.50
McDermott	75.00

MISCELLANEOUS

Date and Description	Buying Price
Evening Globe	.50
Agincourt Dairy One Quart	7.50
Agincourt Dairy One Pint	7.50
Weir and Larminie Encased Postage Stamps	
1, 3, 5, or 10-cent	150.00

ANCHOR MONEY

Date and Description	Buying Price
1/2 Dollar	25.00
1/4 Dollar	1.25
1/8 Dollar	1.00
1/16 Dollar	1.00

IMPORTANT
Buying prices are listed for coins graded VG or better. Bent, damaged or badly worn coins are not collectable and bring no premium value.

CANADIAN MEDALS

WAR MEDALS

Military General Service Medal

Canadian General Service Medal

Egyptian Medal

Date and Description	Buying Price
Military General Service Medal 1812-1814	
Fort Detroit Bar	525.00
Chateauguay Bar	525.00
Chrysler's Farm Bar	750.00
Canadian General Service Medal	
Fenian Raid Bar 1866	75.00
Fenian Raid Bar 1870	175.00
Red River Bar 1870	200.00
Egyptian Medal *	
The Nile Bar	400.00
Kirbekan Bar	400.00

*Awarded to Canadian Boatmen

Khedive's
Bronze
Star

1914
Star

North West
Canada
Medal

1914-1915
Star

South
Africa

British
War
Medal

Date and Description	Buying Price	Date and Description	Buying Price
Khedive's Bronze Star 1884	15.00	1914 Star*	500.00
North West Canada Medal 1885	100.00	1914-1915 Star	1.00
Saskatchewan Bar	200.00	British War Medal	5.00
Queen's South Africa 1899-1900 on reverse	1,000.00	*Canadian Star awarded to 2nd. Field Hospital only.	
Dates removed	15.00		
King's South Africa	15.00		

Allied
Victory
Medal

1939-1945
Atlantic
Air Crew
Europe
Africa
France and
Germany
Italy
Pacific
Burma

Merchantile
Marine
War
Medal

The
Defence
Medal

WORLD WAR II

Canadian
Volunteer
Service
Medal

WW II
1939-1945
War
Medal

Date and Description	Buying Price
1939-1945 Star	1.00
Atlantic Star	1.00
Air Crew Europe	15.00
Africa Star	1.00
France and Germany Star	1.00
Italy Star	1.00
Pacific Star	1.00
Burma Star	1.00
Defence Medal	5.00
1939-1945 War Medal	5.00

Date and Description	Buying Price
Allied Victory Medal 1919	1.00
Merchantile Marine War Medal 1919	5.00
Canadian Volunteer Service Medal 1943	5.00

COMMEMORATIVE MEDALS

Canadian
Korean
Medal

Coronation
Medal-1911

United
Nations
Korea
Medal

Silver
Jubilee
Medal-1935

United
Nations
Emergency
Medal

Coronation
Medal-1937

Date and Description	Buying Price	Date and Description	Buying Price
Canadian Korean War Medal	20.00	King George V Coronation Medal - 1911	7.00
United Nations Korea Medal 1950 (French English)	10.00	King George Silver Jubilee Medal - 1935	7.00
United Nations Emergency Force 1956	10.00	King George VI Coronation Medal - 1937	7.00
United Nations Medal 1960 to present	10.00		
International Commission Medal 1967	10.00		
1973	10.00		

Coronation
Medal-1953

Victoria
Cross

Silver
Jubilee
Medal-1977

Distinguished
Service
Order

Canadian
Centennial
Medal-1967

Date and Description	Buying Price
Queen Elizabeth II Coronation Medal 1953	10.00
Queen Elizabeth II Silver Jubilee Medal 1977	10.00
Canadian Centennial Medal 1967	10.00

Order
of
Canada

Date and Description	Buying Price
Victoria Cross	10,000.00
Distinguished Service Order	250.00
Order of Canada Officer	250.00
Member	500.00
Companion	2,500.00

PAPER MONEY OF CANADA

PROVINCE OF CANADA

1866 ISSUES

nom.	Issue Date	Buying Price	Denom.	Issue Date	Buying Price
	1866	100.00	$10	1866	300.00
2	1866	125.00	$20	1866	300.00
5	1866	200.00	$50	1866	300.00

DOMINION OF CANADA

1870 ISSUES

Denom.		Issue Date	Buying Price
25-cent	Plain	1870	3.00
25-cent	Series A	1870	4.00
25-cent	Series B	1870	20.00

Plain   Series Letter "A"   Series Letter "B"

1870 ISSUES

Denom.	Issue Date	Variety/Signature	Buying Price
$1	1870	Payable at Montreal or Toronto	50.0
$1	1870	Payable at Halifax	125.0
$1	1870	Payable at St. John	150.0
$2	1870	Payable at Montreal or Toronto	175.0
$2	1870	Payable at Halifax or St. John	200.0

1878 ISSUES

Denom.	Issue Date	Variety/Signature	Buying Price
$1	1878	Scalloped Frame Payable at Montreal or Toronto	55.00
$1	1878	Scalloped Frame Payable at St. John or Halifax	100.00
$1	1878	Lettered Frame Payable at Montreal or Toronto	10.00
$1	1878	Lettered Frame Payable at St. John or Halifax	100.00
$2	1878	Payable at Montreal or Toronto	100.00
$2	1878	Payable at St. John or Halifax	175.00

1882 AND 1887 ISSUES

Denom.	Issue Date	Variety/Signature	Buying Price
$4	1882		50.0
$2	1887	Plain, Series A	40.0

1897 AND 1898 ISSUES

No "One"

Inward "One"

Outward "One"

Denom.	Issue Date	Variety/Signature	Buying Price
$1	1897	Green Face Tint	25.00
$2	1897	Red-Brown Back	30.00
2	1897	Dark Brown Back	10.00
$1	1898	ONE Inward	10.00
$1	1898	ONE Outward	6.00

1900 AND 1902 ISSUES

"4" on top

"Four" on top

Denom.	Issue Date	Variety/Signature	Buying Price
5-cent	1900	Courtney	1.00
5-cent	1900	Bouville	1.00
5-cent	1900	Saunders	2.00
4	1900		40.00
4	1902	4 on Top	50.00
4	1902	Four on Top	35.00

1911 AND 1912 ISSUES

Denom.	Issue Date	Variety/Signature	Buying Price
$1	1911	Green Line/Black Line Series	4.00
$5	1912	No Seal	12.00
$5	1912	Seal Over Five	20.00
$5	1912	Seal Only	12.00

1914 - 1917 ISSUES

Denom.	Issue Date	Variety/Signature	Buying Price
$2	1914	No Seal	7.00
$2	1914	Seal Over Two	22.00
$2	1914	Seal Only	13.00
$1	1917	No Seal	3.00
$1	1917	With Seal	5.00

1923 ISSUES

Denom.	Issue Date	Variety/Signature	Buying Price
25-cent	1923	Hyndman/Saunders	3.00
25-cent	1923	McCavour/Saunders	1.00
25-cent	1923	Campbell/Clark	1.00
$1	1923	Various Colour Seals	2.00
$1	1923	Purple Seal	25.00
$2	1923	Various Colour Seals	4.00
$2	1923	Green Seal	8.00
$2	1923	Bronze Seal	6.00

1924 ISSUES

Denom.	Issue Date	Variety/Signature	Buying Price
$5	1924	Queen Mary	75.00

BANK OF CANADA

1935 ISSUES

Denom.	Variety	Buying Price
$ 1	French text	1.5
$ 2	English text	2.0
$ 2	French text	5.0
$ 5	English text	7.0
$ 5	French text	9.0
$ 10	English text	12.0
$ 10	French text	15.0
$ 20	English text, small seal	25.0
$ 20	French text	25.0
$ 25	English text	150.0
$ 25	French text	250.0
$ 50	English text	60.0
$ 50	French text	65.0
$100	English text	110.0
$100	French text	120.0

1937 ISSUES

Gordon	Coyne	Osbourne

| | VF Buying Price | | |
Denom.	Gordon	Coyne	Osbourne
1	1.25	1.25	2.50
2	2.50	2.50	4.00
5	5.25	5.25	20.00
10	10.00	10.00	13.00
20	20.00	20.00	23.00
50	50.00	50.00	60.00
100	100.00	100.00	105.00
1,000	–	–	1,025.00

IMPORTANT

Bank notes with tears, missing corners, pinholes and folding creases are not considered to e very fine (VF) and will bring less.

Devils
Face
Portrait

Modified
Portrait

Asterisk Serial Number   *＃0013980

DEVILS FACE PORTRAIT

	Uncirculated Buying Price			
Denom.	Coyne/ Towers	Coyne/ Towers Asterisk	Beattie/ Coyne	Beatti Coyr
$ 1	2.00	50.00	2.00	20.
$ 2	3.00	40.00	3.50	25.
$ 5	6.00	190.00	5.00	110.
$ 10	11.00	50.00	10.00	40.
$ 20	30.00	110.00	20.00	50.
$ 50	50.00	–	50.00	
$ 100	100.00	–	100.00	
$1,000	1,025.00	–	–	

MODIFIED PORTRAIT

	Uncirculated Buying Price	
Denom.	Beattie/Coyne	Beattie/Coyr Asteri
$ 1	1.75	2.
$ 2	2.15	3.
$ 5	5.25	6.
$ 10	10.00	10.
$ 20	20.00	20.
$ 50	50.00	
$ 100	100.00	
$1,000	–	

IMPORTANT

Bank notes to qualify as uncirculated must be in new condition with no folds or crease
Colour must be fresh and the notes crisp.

$1 CENTENNIAL 1967

For the centennial of Canada's Confederation a special $1 note was issued. The note had a single design and two types of serial numbers, regular serial numbers and a special number 1867 - 1967. The special series was available from the Bank of Canada as a collector's item, but examples were soon found in circulation. In addition there was an asterisk series for replacement notes.

Denom.	Issue Date	Variety/Signature	Buying Price Unc
$1	1967	Commemorative serial number	1.00
$1	1967	Regular serial number	1.00
$1	1967	Asterisk serial number	1.50

1969 - 1975 ISSUE

This new series combined fine line engraving with subtle colour variations to make notes that are extremely difficult to counterfeit. The series features a new portrait of the Queen, and portraits of some of the previous prime ministers of Canada. To date the notes from $1 through $100 have been released in both regular and asterisk issues. The first notes issued in the series were the $20 dated 1969 (despite their date they were released first in June, 1970).

The serial number appears twice on the face of the notes, upper left in red and upper right in blue.

1979 ISSUES

The series beginning in 1979 is a modification of the previous issue. The face designs are similar, as is the colouration. The serial numbers are moved to the back of the note at the bottom where the name of the Bank of Canada previously appeared. The black serial numbers are machine readable.

Notes from 1969 to date do not command a numismatic premium above face value.

1986 ISSUE

On March 14, 1986, the Bank of Canada introduced a new series of banknotes. The new designs were launched that year with the issue of the $2 and $5 notes. The Bank of Canada was not undertaken a redesign of the $1 note because of the Government of Canada's decision to introduce the new one-dollar coin for circulation. The $1 note will be phased out beginning in 1989.

This series of notes incorporates new security features against counterfeiting as well as changes which will facilitate more efficient use of high-speed note sorting machines. In addition the series incorporates features to assist the blind and visually impaired to distinguish among denomination of notes.

NEWFOUNDLAND GOVERNMENT PUBLIC WORKS CASH NOTES

TYPE 1

Denom.	Buying Price
40-cents	35.00
50-cents	35.00
80-cents	40.00
$1	50.00
$5	75.00

TYPE 2

Denom.	Buying Price
25-cents	10.00
50-cents	10.00
$1	20.00
$2	50.00
$5	100.00

NEWFOUNDLAND GOVERNMENT NOTES

Denom.	Buying Price
$1	8.00
$2	12.00

CANADIAN NOTE-ISSUING BANKS

The following list of banks identifies in alphabetical order all the non-government banks which issued or ordered Canadian notes.

Bank notes were first issued in Canada in 1813 and continued until 1943. One hundred and sixty different banks issued notes and some over a long period of time. There are literally thousands of different notes and if you add different grades, the number rises to tens of thousands. Far beyond the scope of this guide.

If you have a bank note that is on this list of banks then it is Canadian and please check with your local coin dealer for current buying prices.

The Bank of Acadia, Liverpool, N.S., 1872-1873
The Accommodation Bank, Kingston, U.C., 1836-1837
The Agricultural Bank, Montreal, L.C. 1837,
The Agricultural Bank, Toronto, U.C. 1834-1837
Arman's Bank, Montreal, L.C., 1837
Barclay's Bank (Canada), Montreal, Que., 1929-1956
La Banque du Boucherville, Boucherville, L.C., 1830's
The Bank of Brantford, Brantford, C.W., 1857-1860's
The British Canadian Bank, Toronto, Ont., 1883-1884
The Bank of British Columbia, Victoria, B.C., 1862-1901
The Bank of British North America, 1836-1918
Canada Bank, Montreal, L.C., 1792
The Canada Bank, Toronto, C.W., 1855
The Bank of Canada, Montreal, L.C., 1813-1831
The Canadian Bank of Commerce, Toronto,Ont., 1867-1961
Banque Canadienne, St. Hyacinthe, L.C., 1836-1838
Banque Canadienne Nationale, Montreal, Que., 1924-1979
The Central Bank of Canada, Toronto, Ont., 1883-1887
Central Bank of New Brunswick, Fredericton, N.B., 1834-1866
Charlotte County Bank, St. Andrew's, N.B., 1825-1865
Bank of Charlottetown, Charlottetown, P.E.I., 1852
The City Bank, Montreal, L.C., 1833-1876
City Bank, Saint John, N.B., 1836-1839
The Bank of Clifton, C.W., 1859-1863
The Colonial Bank of Canada, Toronto, C.W., 1856-1863
The Colonial Bank of Chatham, Chatham, U.C., 1837-1839
Commercial Bank, Brockville, U.C., 1837
Commerical Bank, Kingston, U.C., 1837
The Commercial Bank of Canada, Kingston, C.W., 1856-1868
The Commercial Bank of Fort Erie, Fort Erie, U.C., 1836-1839
The Commercial Bank of Lake Ontario, Niagara Falls, U.C., 1837
The Commercial Bank of Manitoba, Winnipeg, Man., 1885-1893
The Commercial Bank of the Midland District, Kingston, U.C., 1831-1856
Commercial Bank of Montreal, Montreal, L.C., 1835-1837
Commercial Bank of New Brunswick, Saint John, N.B., 1834-1868
The Commercial Bank of Newfoundland, St. John's Nfld., 1857-1894
Commercial Bank of Windsor, Windsor, N.S., 1864-1902
Commercial Branch Bank of Canada, Collingwood, C.W., 1861-1879
The Consolidated Bank of Canada, Montreal, Que., 1876-1879
The Bank of the County of Elgin, St. Thomas, C.W., 1857-1862
The Crown Bank of Canada, Toronto, Ont., 1904-1908
The Dominion Bank, Toronto, Ont., 1869-1955
Eastern Bank of Canada, Saint John, N.B., 1928-1934
The Eastern Townships Bank, Sherbrooke, C.E., 1855-1912
The Exchange Bank, Quebec, L.C., 1840's

The Exchange Bank of Canada, Montreal, Que., 1871-1883
The Exchange Bank of Canada, Windsor, Ont., 1860's
The Exchange Bank of Toronto, C.W., 1855
The Exchange Bank of Yarmouth, Yarmouth, N.S., 1867-1903
The Exchange Bank Company of Chippewa, Chippewa, U.C., 1837
The Farmer's Bank, Toronto, U.C., 1840's
The Farmers Bank of Canada, Toronto, Ont., 1906-1910
The Farmer's Bank of Malden, Malden, U.C., 1840's
The Farmer's Joint Stock Banking Co., Toronto, U.C., 1835-1849
The Farmers J.S. Banking Co., Toronto, U.C., 1830's
The Farmers Bank of Rustico, Rustico, P.E.I., 1862-1892
The Farmers Bank of St. John's, St. John's, L.C., 1837-1838
The Federal Bank of Canada, Toronto, Ont., 1874-1888
The Bank of Fredericton, Fredericton, N.B., 1836-1839
The Free Holders Bank of the Midland District, Bath, U.C., 1837
Goderich Bank, Goderich, U.C., 1834
The Gore Bank, Hamilton, U.C., 1835-1870
The Gore Bank of Hamilton, Hamilton, U.C., ca. 1837
The Grenville County Bank, Prescott, C.W., 1856
The Halifax Banking Company, Halifax, N.S., 1825-1903
The Hamilton Bank, Hamilton, L.C., 1835
The Bank of Hamilton, Hamilton, Ont. 1872-1923
Hart's Bank, Three Rivers, L.C., 1835-1847
Henry's Bank, La Prairie and Montreal, L.C., 1837
Banque d'Hochelaga, Montreal, Que., 1873-1925
The Home Bank of Canada, Toronto, Ont., 1903-1923
The Bank of Hull, Hull, L.C., 1837
The Imperial Bank of Canada, Toronto, Ont., 1873-1961
The International Bank of Canada, Toronto, U.C., 1858-1859
Banque Internationale du Canada, Montreal, Que., 1911-1913
La Banque Jacques Cartier, Montreal, C.E., 1861-1900
The Kingston Bank, Kingston, L.C., 1837
The Bank of Liverpool, Liverpool, N.S., 1871-1879
The Bank of London in Canada, London, Ont., 1883-1888
Lower Canada Bank, Montreal, L.C., 1837
The Bank of Lower Canada, Quebec, L.C., late 1830's
MacDonald & Co., Victoria, B.C., 1859-1866
The Maritime Bank of the Dominion of Canada, Saint John, N.B., 1872-1887
The Mechanics Bank, Montreal, L.C., 1837
The Mechanics Bank, Montreal, C.E., 1865-1879
The Mechanics Bank of Saint John's, Saint John's, L.C., 1837
The Merchantile Banking Corporation, Halifax, N.S., 1878
The Merchants Bank, Montreal, C.E., 1864-1868
The Merchants Bank, Toronto, U.C., 1837
The Merchants Bank of Canada, Montreal, Que., 1868-1923
The Merchants Bank of Halifax, Halifax, N.S., 1864-1901
The Merchants Bank of Prince Edward Island, Charlottetown, P.E.I., 1871-1906
The Merchants Exchange Bank, Goderich, C.W., 1853
The Metropolitan Bank, Montreal, Que., 1871-1876
The Metropolitan Bank, Toronto., 1902-1914
The Molsons Bank, Montreal, C.E., 1837-1925
Montreal Bank, Montreal, L.C., 1817-1822
The Montreal Bank, Montreal, C.W., 1840's-1850's
The Bank of Montreal, Montreal, L.C., 1822 to date
La Banque Nationale, Montreal, C.E., 1860-1925
The Bank of New Brunswick, Saint John, N.B. 1820-1913
The Newcastle Banking Co., Amherst, U.C., 1836

The Newcastle District Loan Company, Peterborough, U.C., 1836
The Niagara District Bank, St. Catharines, C.W., 1853-1875
The Niagara Suspension Bridge Bank, Queenston, U.C., 1836-1841
The Northern Bank, Winnipeg, Man., 1905-1908
The Northern Crown Bank, Winnipeg, Man., 1908-1918
The Bank of Nova Scotia, Halifax, N.S., 1832 to date
The Ontario Bank, Bowmanvile, C.W., 1857-1906
The Bank of Ottawa, Montreal, L.C., 1837
The Bank of Ottawa, Ottawa, Ont., 1874-1919
The Bank of the People, Toronto, U.C., 1835-1841
La Banque du Peuple, Montreal,, L.C., 1835-1895
The People's Bank of Halifax, Halifax, N.S., 1864-1905
The People's Bank of New Brunswick, Fredericton, N.B., 1864-1907
The Pheonix Bank, Phillipsburg, L.C., 1837-1841
The Pictou Bank, Pictou, N.S., 1873-1887
The Bank of Prince Edward Island, Charlottetown, P.E.I., 1856-1881
The Provincial Bank, London, Ont., 1884
The Provincial Bank of Canada, Stanstead, Ont., 1856-1863
La Banque Provinciale du Canada, Montreal, Quec., 1900-1979
The Quebec Bank, Quebec, L.C., 1818-1917
Bank of Quebec Lower Canada, Quebec, L.C., 1841
The Royal Bank of Canada, Montreal, Que., 1901 to date
The Royal Canadian Bank, Toronto, C.W., 1864-1876
The Saint Francis Bank, Stanstead, C.E., 1855
La Banque de St. Hyacinthe, St. Hycainthe, Que., 1873-1908
La Banque de St. Jean, St. Jean, Que., 1873-1908
Banque St. Jean Baptiste, Montreal, Que., 1875
The St. Lawrence Bank, Toronto, Ont., 1872-1876
The St. Lawrence Bank & Lumber Co., Malbaie, L.C., 1837
The St. Stephen's Bank, St. Stephen, N.B., 1836-1910
The Bank of Saskatchewan, Moose Jaw, Sask., 1913
The Sovereign Bank of Canada, Montreal, Que., 1901-1908
The Stadacona Bank, Quebec City, Que., 1872-1879
The Standard Bank of Canada, Toronto, Ont., 1876-1928
The Sterling Bank of Canada, Toronto, Ont., 1905-1924
The Summerside Bank, Summerside, P.E.I., 1866-1901
Tattersall Bank, Montreal, L.C., 183-
The Bank of Toronto, Toronto, Ont., 1855-1954
The Traders Bank of Canada, Toronto, Ont., 1885-1912
The Union Bank, Montreal, L.C., 1838-ca 1840
The Union Bank of Canada, Quebec City, Que., 1886-1925
The Union Bank of Halifax, Halifax, N.S., 1856-1910
The Union Bank of Lower Canada, Quebec, C.E., 1865-1886
The Union Bank of Montreal, Montreal, L.C., ca 1840
Union Bank of Newfoundland, St. John's, Nfld., 1854-1894
The Union Bank of Prince Edward Island, Charlottetown, P.E.I., 1860-1893
United Empire Bank of Canada, Toronto, Ont., 1906-1911
Bank of Upper Canada, Kingston, U.C., 1819-1822
Bank of Upper Canada, York, U.C., 1821-1866
The Bank of Vancouver, Vancouver, B.C., 1910-1914
The Bank of Victoria, Victoria, U.C., 1836
La Banque Ville Marie, Montreal, Que., 1872-1899
The Bank of Western Canada, Clifton, C.W., 1859-1863
The Western Bank of Canada, Oshawa, Ont., 1882-1909
The Westmoreland Bank of New Brunswick, N.B., 1854-1867
The Weyburn Security Bank, Weyburn, Sask., 1910-1931
The Bank of Yarmouth, Yarmouth, N.S., 1859-1905
The Zimmerman Bank, Elgin, C.W., 1854-1859

COINS OF THE UNITED STATES

MINT MARKS

The United States decimal coinage is identified by the following mint marks:

C -Charlotte, North Carolina
CC -Carson City, Nevada
D -Dahlonega, Georgia(gold coins only)
D -Denver, Colorado(1906 to date)
O -New Orleans, Louisiana
S -San Francisco, California
P -Philadelphia, Pennsylvania

HALF CENTS

Liberty Cap

Classic Head

Date and Mint Mark	Buying Price
1793	450.00
1794	75.00
1795	50.00
1796	900.00
1797	50.00

Date and Mint Mark	Buying Price
1809 to 1810	4.00
1811	20.00
1825 to 1835	4.00

Braided Hair

Draped Bust

Date and Mint Mark	Buying Price
1849 to 1857	6.00

Date and Mint Mark	Buying Price
1800	5.00
1802	35.00
1803-1808	4.00

IMPORTANT
Do not clean your coins. Coins should be handled carefully. Only experts should consider cleaning. If you are not an expert the results can be disasterous.

LARGE CENTS

Flowing Hair

Date and Mint Mark	Buying Price
1793	200.00

Liberty Cap

Date and Mint Mark	Buying Price
1793	200.00
1794	30.00
1795	25.00
1796	30.00

Draped Bust

Date and Mint Mark	Buying Price
1796	20.00
1797	10.00
1798	5.00
1799	200.00
1800 to 1803	4.00
1803 Large Date	125.00
1804	125.00
1805 to 1807	4.00

Classic Head

Date and Mint Mark	Buying Price
1808	8.00
1809	20.00
1810	6.00
1811	15.00
1812 to 1814	6.00

Coronet Head

Date and Mint Mark	Buying Price
1816 to 1820	1.00
1821	3.00
1822	1.00
1823	5.00
1824 to 1838	1.00
1839 to 1856	.75
1857	4.00

SMALL CENTS

Flying Eagle

Date and Mint Mark	Buying Price
1856	300.00
1857 to 1858	.50

Indian Head

Date and Mint Mark	Buying Price
1859 to 1865	.35
1866 to 1868	2.00
1869 to 1872	4.00
1873 to 1876	1.00
1877	40.00
1878 to 1886	.35
1887 to 1908	.10
1908S	4.00
1909	.10
1909S	20.00

Lincoln Head Wheat Ears

Date and Mint Mark	Buying Price
1909	.03
1909VDB	.10
1909S	5.00
1909SVDB	40.00
19010 to 1914	.03
1914D	10.00
1915D to 1931D	.02
1931S	5.00
1932-1954	.01

Lincoln Head Memorial

Date and Mint Mark	Buying Price
1955 Double Date	20.00
1955 to 1988	.01

TWO CENTS

Date and Mint Mark	Buying Price
1864 to 1872	.35
1873	10.00

THREE CENTS

Silver

Date and Mint Mark	Buying Price
1851 to 1862	.75
1863 to 1873	100.00

Nickel

Date and Mint Mark	Buying Price
1865 to 1874	.30
1875 to 1876	1.00
1877 to 1878	70.00
1879 to 1880	7.00
1881	.30
1882	10.00
1883	20.00
1884 to 1887	50.00
1888 to 1889	7.00

FIVE CENTS NICKEL

Shield

Date and Mint Mark	Buying Price
1866 to 1876	1.00
1879 to 1881	40.00
1882 to 1883	.75

Liberty Head

Date and Mint Mark	Buying Price
1883 to 1884	.30
1885	55.00
1886	12.00
1887 to 1912	.10
1912S	9.00

Indian Head or Buffalo Type

Date and Mint Mark	Buying Price
1913	.10
1913S	12.00
1914 to 1918	.10
1918D 8/7	100.00
1919 to 1938	.10

Jefferson Type

Date and Mint Mark	Buying Price
1938 to 1988	.05

HALF DIMES

Silver

Flowing Hair

Date and Mint Mark	Buying Price
1794 to 1795	175.00

Draped Bust

Date and Mint Mark	Buying Price
1796 to 1797	225.00
1800 to 1801	150.00
1802	1,400.00
1803 to 1805	150.00

Capped Bust

Date and Mint Mark	Buying Price
1829 to 1837	2.50

Liberty Seated

Date and Mint Mark	Buying Price
1837	6.00
1838 No Stars	12.00
1838 to 1845	1.00
1846	35.00
1847 to 1863	1.00
1864	50.00
1864S	1.00
1865	30.00
1866	30.00
1867	40.00
1868	8.00
1869 to 1873	.75

DIMES

Draped Bust

Date and Mint Mark	Buying Price
1796 to 1797	300.00
1798 to 1807	150.00

Capped Bust

Date and Mint Mark	Buying Price
1809 to 1811	10.00
1814 to 1821	4.00
1822	20.00
1823 to 1837	2.00

Liberty Seated

Date and Mint Mark	Buying Price
1837 to 1838	7.00
1839 to 1843	.75
1844	10.00
1845	.75
1846	15.00
1847 to 1856	.75
1856S	10.00
1857 to 1858	.75
1858S	10.00
1859S	15.00
1860O	100.00
1861 to 1862	.75
1863	20.00
1864 to 1867	25.00
1864S to 1867S	2.00
1868 to 1871	.55
1871CC	100.00
1872CC	60.00
1873CC	125.00
1874CC	200.00
1875 to 1878	.55
1878CC	10.00
1879	35.00
1880 to 1881	10.00
1882 to 1885	.55
1885S	25.00
1886 to 1891	.55

Barber

Date and Mint Mark	Buying Price
1892 to 1895	.75
1895O	35.00
1896O	8.00
1897 to 1916	.55

Mercury Head

Date and Mint Mark	Buying Price
1916	.50
1916D	100.00
1917 to 1945	.50

Roosevelt - Silver

Date and Mint Mark	Buying Price
1946 to 1964	.50

Roosevelt - Clad

Date and Mint Mark	Buying Price
1965 to 1988	.10

TWENTY CENTS

Date and Mint Mark	Buying Price
1875 to 1878	7.00
1877 to 1878 Proof	1,000.00

QUARTER DOLLAR

Draped Bust

Date and Mint Mark	Buying Price
1796	800.00
1804	150.00
1805 to 1807	40.00

Capped Bust

Date and Mint Mark	Buying Price
1815 to 1822	12.00
1823	1,200.00
1824 to 1838	7.00

Liberty Seated

Date and Mint Mark	Buying Price
1838 to 1849	2.50
1849O	90.00
1850 to 1851	4.00
1851O	45.00
1852	4.00
1852O	60.00

Date and Mint Mark	Buying Price
1853 No Arrows	40.00
1865 to 1870	1.50
1870CC	400.00
1871CC	180.00
1871S	50.00
1872CC	70.00
1874 to 1878	1.50
1879 to 1888	12.00
1889 to 1891	1.40

Barber

Date and Mint Mark	Buying Price
1892 to 1896	1.25
1896S	50.00
1897 to 1901	1.25
1901S	300.00
1902 to 1913	1.25
1913S	70.00
1914 to 1916	1.25

Standing Liberty

Date and Mint Mark	Buying Price
1916	300.00
1917 to 1930	1.25

Washington - Silver

Date and Mint Mark	Buying Price
1932 to 1964	1.25

Washington - Clad

Date and Mint Mark	Buying Price
1965 to 1975	.25

200th Bi-Centennial

Date and Mint Mark	Buying Price
1976	.25

Washington - Clad

Date and Mint Mark	Buying Price
1977 to 1988	.25

HALF DOLLARS

Flowing Hair

Date and Mint Mark	Buying Price
1794	400.00
1795	100.00

Draped Bust

Date and Mint Mark	Buying Price
1796 15 Stars	2,400.00
1796 16 Stars	2,400.00
1797 15 Stars	2,400.00
1801 to 1802	45.00
1803 to 1807	15.00

Capped Bust

Date and Mint Mark	Buying Price
1807	10.00
1808 to 1814	5.00

Date and Mint Mark	Buying Price
1815	175.00
1817 to 1836	5.00
1836 Reeded Edge	100.00
1837 to 1839	5.00
1839O	25.00

Liberty Seated

Date and Mint Mark	Buying Price
1839 to 1849	4.00
1850	10.00
1851	10.00
1852	20.00
1852O	10.00
1853 to 1855	3.00
1855S Arrows	75.00
1856 to 1870	3.00
1870CC	100.00
1871 and 1871S	3.00
1871CC	20.00
1872CC to 1878CC	10.00
1878S	800.00
1879 to 1890	20.00
1891	3.00

Barber

Date and Mint Mark	Buying Price
1892	3.00
1892O and 1892S	20.00
1893 to 1897	2.50
1897S	20.00
1898 to 1915	2.40

Liberty Walking

Date and Mint Mark	Buying Price
1916 to 1920	2.40
1921	15.00
1921D	20.00
1923 to 1947	2.40

Franklin

Date and Mint Mark	Buying Price
1948 to 1963	2.40

Kennedy Silver

Date and Mint Mark	Buying Price
1964	2.40

Kennedy Silver Clad

Date and Mint Mark	Description	Buying Price
1965 to 1970		1.00

Kennedy Copper Clad

Date and Mint Mark	Buying Price
1971 to 1988	.50

SILVER DOLLARS

Flowing Hair

Date and Mint Mark	Buying Price
1794	1,800.00
1795	160.00

Draped Bust

Date and Mint Mark	Buying Price
1795	300.00
1796 to 1798	400.00
1798 to 1803	200.00

Liberty Seated

Date and Mint Mark	Buying Price
1840 to 1871	25.00
1871CC	175.00
1872	25.00
1872CC	75.00
1872S	40.00
1873	25.00
1873CC	100.00

Liberty Head

Date and Mint Mark	Buying Price
1878 to 1892	7.00
1879CC to 1881CC	20.00
1882CC to 1884CC	10.00
1885CC	40.00
1889CC	80.00
1893CC	30.00
1893O	25.00
1893S	400.00
1894	100.00
1895O	25.00
1895S	40.00
1896 to 1903	7.00
1903O	40.00
1904 to 1921	6.00

Peace

Date and Mint Mark	Buying Price
1921 to 1927	6.00
1928	30.00
1928S to 1935	6.00

Eisenhower

Date and Mint Mark	Buying Price
1971 to 1976	1.00

Susan B. Anthony

Date and Mint Mark	Buying Price
1979 to 1981	1.00

TRADE DOLLARS

Date and Mint Mark	Buying Price
1873 to 1878	15.00
1878CC	40.00

GOLD COINS

DOLLARS

Type 1 Liberty Head

Date and Mint Mark	Buying Price
1849 to 1854	110.00

Type 2 Indian Head Small

Date and Mint Mark	Buying Price
1854 to 1855	175.00
1855C	300.00
1855D	1,000.00

Type 3 Indian Head Large

Date and Mint Mark	Buying Price
1855 to 1889	90.00
1856D	900.00
1860D	900.00
1861D	2,000.00
1875	900.00

QUARTER EAGLES (2 1/2 DOLLARS)

Capped Bust Right

Date and Mint Mark	Buying Price
1796	3,700.00
1797 to 1807	1,000.00

Capped Bust Left

Date and Mint Mark	Buying Price
1808	3,500.00

Capped Head Left

Date and Mint Mark	Buying Price
1821 to 1827	1,150.00
1829 to 1833	900.00
1834	2,500.00

Classic Head

Date and Mint Mark	Buying Price
1834 to 1839	150.00

Coronet Head

Date and Mint Mark	Buying Price
1840 to 1907	100.00
1841 Proof	5,000.00
1843C S/D Cr 4	325.00
1848 California	1,500.00
1854D	1,000.00
1855D	1,000.00
1856D	1,200.00
1875	800.00

Indian Head

Date and Mint Mark	Buying Price
1908 to 1929	100.00
1911D	300.00

3 DOLLARS

Date and Mint Mark	Buying Price
1854 to 1858	240.00
1854D	2000.00
1880 to 1889	100.00
1873 Closed 3	1,000.00
1881	500.00

4 DOLLARS

Date and Mint Mark	Buying Price
1879 to 1880	8,000.00

HALF EAGLES (5 DOLLARS)

Capped Bust Right

Date and Mint Mark	Buying Price
1795 to 1797	2,000.00
1798 to 1807	500.00

Draped Bust Left

Date and Mint Mark	Buying Price
1807 to 1834	500.00
1821	1,500.00
1823	1,000.00
1824	2,000.00
1825	1,500.00
1826	1,700.00
1827	2,500.00
1828	2,500.00
1829	2,500.00

Classic Head

Date and Mint Mark	Buying Price
1834 to 1838	125.00
1838C	400.00
1838D	400.00

Coronet Head

Date and Mint Mark	Buying Price
1839 to 1908	120.00
1861C	400.00
1861D	1,000.00
1870CC	1,000.00
1878CC	600.00

Indian Head

Date and Mint Mark	Buying Price
1908 to 1916	140.00
1929	1,000.00

EAGLE (10 DOLLARS)

Capped Bust Right

Date and Mint Mark	Buying Price
Small Eagle, 1795 to 1797	2,000.00
Heraldic, Eagle, 1797 to 1804	1,000.00

Coronet Head

Date and Mint Mark	Buying Price
1838 to 1907	275.00
1859O	600.00
1863	1,000.00
1864S	900.00
1866S	500.00
1870CC	600.00
1873	600.00
1873CC	500.00
1876	600.00
1877	800.00
1877CC	500.00
1878CC	500.00
1879CC	1,200.00
1879O	600.00
1883O	1,000.00

Indian Head

Date and Mint Mark	Buying Price
1907 to 1933	275.00
1920S	2,000.00
1930S	1,200.00

DOUBLE EAGLES ($20 DOLLARS)

Liberty

Date and Mint Mark	Buying Price
1849 to 1907	550.00
1855O	1,000.00
1859O	800.00
1860O	1,100.00
1861O	600.00
1870CC	7,000.00
1871CC	700.00
1879O	1,200.00
1881	1,100.00
1882	1,700.00
1885	1,700.00
1886	2,000.00
1891	600.00
1891CC	600.00
1892	500.00

St Gaudens

Date and Mint Mark	Buying Price
1907 MCMVII	1,800.00
1907 to 1916	550.00
1920S	3,000.00
1921	3,800.00
1922 to 1928	550.00
1927D	25,000.00
1927S	1,000.00
1929	1,200.00
1930 to 1932	2,000.00

US Gold coins must be in VF or better condition, badly worn or damaged coins will be discounted from these prices.

GOLD COMMEMORATIVE COINS

Date and Mint Mark	Buying Price
1903 $1 Louisiana Purchase Jefferson	90.00
1903 $1 Louisiana Purchase McKinley	90.00
1904 $1 Louis & Clark Exposition	115.00
1905 $1 Louis & Clark Exposition	115.00
1915S $1 Panama-Pacific Exposition	90.00
1916 $1 McKinley Memorial	90.00
1917 $1 McKinley Memorial	90.00
1922 $1 Grant Memorial, With star	100.00
1922 $1 Grant Memorial, Without star	100.00
1915S $2.50 Panama-Pacific Exposition	250.00
1926 $2.50 Philadelphia Sesquicentennial	190.00

WORLD GOLD COINS

This partial listing of world gold coins indicates the prices dealers are willing to pay based on the Canadian dollar gold price as at January 19th, 1988. Prices will fluctuate with the market price of gold plus the Canadian/U.S. dollar exchange.

AUSTRIA

Date and Denom.	Fine Gold Content oz	Buying Price
1912 10K	0.0980	50.00
1915 20K	0.1960	102.50
1915 100K	0.9803	510.00
1915 1D	0.1109	57.50
1914 4D	0.4438	230.00
1892 10Fr	0.0933	47.50
1892 20Fr*	0.1867	97.50

BAHAMAS

Date and Denom.	Fine Gold Content oz	Buying Price
1967 $ 10	0.1177	60.00
1971 $ 10	0.1177	60.00
1972 $ 10	0.0940	47.50
1967 $ 20	0.2355	122.50
1971 $ 20*	0.2355	122.50
1972 $ 20	0.1880	97.50
1967 $ 50	0.5888	305.00
1971 $ 50	0.5888	305.00
1972 $ 50	0.4708	245.00
1967 $100	1.1776	610.00
1971 $100	1.1776	610.00
1972 $100	0.9420	490.00

BELGUIM

Date and Denom.	Fine Gold Content oz	Buying Price
1867 to 1914 20Fr	0.1867	97.50

BERMUDA

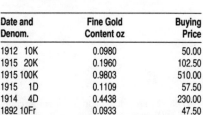

Date and Denom.	Fine Gold Content oz	Buying Price
1970 $ 20	0.2355	122.50
1977 $ 50	0.1172	60.00
1975 $100*	0.2034	105.00
1977 $100	0.2344	122.50

CAYMAN ISLANDS

Date and Denom.	Fine Gold Content oz	Buying Price
1972 $ 25*	0.2532	130.0
1974 $ 50	0.1823	95.0
1974 $100	0.3646	190.0
1975 $100	0.3646	190.0
1977 $100	0.3646	190.0

CHILE

Date and Denom.	Fine Gold Content oz	Buying Price
1898 to 1900 5p	0.0883	45.00
1896 to 1901 10p*	0.1766	90.00
1896 to 1917 20p	0.3532	185.00
1926 to 1980 100p	0.5886	305.00

GERMANY

Date and Denom.	Fine Gold Content oz	Buying Price
1872 to 1914 10 DM	0.1152	60.00
1871 to 1914 20 DM*	0.2304	120.00

COLUMBIA

Date and Denom.	Fine Gold Content oz	Buying Price
1913 to 1929 2 1/2p	0.1177	60.00
1913 to 1930 5p	0.2355	122.50
1919 and 1924 10p	0.4710	245.00
1973 1500p*	0.5527	287.50

GREAT BRITAIN

Date and Denom.	Fine Gold Content oz	Buying Price
1863 to 1915 ½ Sov.	0.1177	60.00
1871 to 1968 Sov*	0.2354	120.00
1887 Two Pound	0.4708	245.00
1897 Two Pound	0.4708	245.00
1902 Two Pound	0.4708	245.00
1911 Two Pound	0.4708	245.00
1937 Two Pound	0.4708	245.00
1887 Five Pound	1.1773	610.00
1897 Five Pound	1.1773	610.00
1902 Five Pound	1.1773	610.00
1911 Five Pound	1.1773	610.00
1937 Five Pound	1.1773	610.00

FRANCE

Date and Denom.	Fine Gold Content oz	Buying Price
1856 to 1869 5Fr	0.0467	25.00
1854 to 1914 10Fr	0.0933	50.00
1809 to 1914 20Fr*	0.1867	97.50
1810 to 1838 40Fr	0.3734	195.00
1855 to 1864 50Fr	0.4667	242.50
1855 to 1913 100Fr	0.9335	485.00

IRAN

Date and Denom.	Fine Gold Content oz	Buying Price
1971 500R	0.1883	97.50
1971 750R*	0.2827	147.50
1971 1000R	0.3770	195.00
1971 2000R	0.7541	390.00

ITALY

Date and Denom.	Fine Gold Content oz	Buying Price
1932 to 1860 10L	0.0931	47.50
1831 to 1860 20L*	0.1866	97.50
1822 to 1831 40L	0.3733	195.00
1832 to 1844 100L	0.9332	485.00

NETHERLANDS

Date and Denom.	Fine Gold Content oz	Buying Price
1900 to 1937 1D*	0.1109	57.50
1912 5G	0.0973	50.00
1875 to 1933 10G	0.1947	100.00

JAMAICA

Date and Denom.	Fine Gold Content oz	Buying Price
1972 $ 20*	0.2531	130.00
1975, 1976 $100	0.2265	117.50
1978 $100	0.3281	170.00
1978, 1979 $250	1.2507	650.00

PANAMA

Date and Denom.	Fine Gold Content oz	Buying Price
1975 to 1979 100B*	0.2361	122.50
1975 to 1979 500B	1.2067	625.00

RUSSIA

Date and Denom.	Fine Gold Content oz	Buying Price
1897 to 1911 5R*	0.1244	65.00
1897 7 1/2R	0.1867	95.00
1898 to 1911 10R	0.2489	130.00
1897 15R	0.3734	195.00
1977 to 1988 100R	0.5000	260.00

MEXICO

Date and Denom.	Fine Gold Content oz	Buying Price
1945 2p	0.0482	77.50
1945 2 1/2p	0.0602	30.00
1955 5p	0.1205	62.50
1959 10p*	0.2411	125.00
1959 20p	0.4823	250.00
1947 50p	1.2057	625.00

Above dates are restrikes

APPENDIX - BULLION VALUES

Silver and gold coins and other numismatic items are often bought by dealers for their bullion value, that is the value of the pure precious metals which they contain. The weight of precious metals is expressed in grams or troy ounces, not in avoirdupois ounces. A troy ounce is greater than an avoirdupois ounce.

$$1 \text{ Troy Ounce} = 31.103 \text{ Grams}$$
$$1 \text{ Avoirdupois Ounce} = 28,349 \text{ Grams}$$

GOLD

The quantity of pure gold in gold coins is calculated by multiplying the gold fineness or purity of the coin by its weight in troy ounces or grams. Gold purity can also be expressed in karats, a 24-part system with 24-karats equalling pure gold, 22 karats equalling 22 parts gold to 2 parts base metal, 18 karats equalling 18 part gold to 6 parts base metal etc.

Karats	Fineness	Purity
24	.999	99.9%
22	.916	91.6%
18	.750	75.0%
14	.585	58.5%
10	.417	41.7%
9	.375	37.5%

A 14-karat or .585 fine gold coin weighing 1 troy ounce contains 1 ounce x .585 = .585 troy ounces of pure gold. If gold is worth $600 per troy ounce, then this coin is worth $600 x .585 = $351. (See extended charts on following pages.)

SILVER

The quantity of pure silver in silver coins is calculated by multiplying the silver fineness or purity of the coin by its weight in troy ounces.

Karats	Fineness	Purity
Pure	.999	99.9%
Fine	.999	99.9%
Sterling	.925	92.5%
Coin	.800	80.0%
Coin	.500	50.0%

A .800 fine silver coin weighing 1 troy ounce contains 1 x .800 = .800 troy ounces or pure silver. If silver is worth $20 and ounce, then this coin is worth $20 x .800 = $16. (See extended charts on following pages.)

GOLD CONTENT OF CANADIAN GOLD COINS

Denom.	Date and Mint Mark	Gross Weight (Grams)	Fineness	Pure Gold Content	
				Grams	Troy Oz.
NEWFOUNDLAND					
$2	1865-1888	3.33	.917	3.05	.100
CANADA					
1 pd.	1908C-1910C	7.99	.917	7.32	.236
1 pd.	1911C-1919C	7.99	.917	7.32	.236
$5	1912-1914	8.36	.900	7.52	2.42
$10	1912-1914	16.72	.900	15.05	.484
$20	1967	18.27	.900	16.45	.529
$5 M.L.	1982-1986	3.11	.9999	3.11	.10
$10 M.L.	1982-1986	7.78	.9999	7.78	.25
$50 M.L.	1979-1986	31.10	.999	31.10	1.00
$100	1976 (Unc.)	13.33	.583	7.78	.25
$100	1976 (Proof)	16.96	.917	15.55	.499
$100	1977-1986	16.96	.917	15.55	.49
$100	1987 (Proof)	13.33	.583	7.78	.25

SILVER CONTENT OF CANADIAN SILVER COINS

Denom.	Date	Fineness	Silver Content	
			Grams	Troy Oz.
$1	1935-1967	.800	18.661	.600
$1	1971-date	.500	11.662	.375
50-cents	1870-1919	.925	10.792	.347
50-cents	1920-1967	.800	9.330	.30
25-cents	1870-1919	.925	5.370	.17
25-cents	1920-1967	.800	4.665	.15
25-cents	1967-1968	.500	2.923	.094
10-cents	1858-1919	.925	2.146	.069
10-cents	1920-1967	.800	1.866	.06
10-cents	1967-1968	.500	1.170	.03
5-cents	1858-1919	.925	1.080	.03
5-cents	1920-1921	.800	.933	.030

BULLION VALUES OF CANADIAN GOLD COINS

(Computed from $300/troy ounce to $700/troy ounce in increments of $100 Canadian)

Denomination	Date and Mint Mark	$300	$400	$500	$600	$700
NEWFOUNDLAND						
$2	1865-1888	30.00	40.00	50.00	60.00	70.00
CANADA						
1 pd.	1908C-1910C	70.95	94.40	118.00	141.60	165.20
1 pd.	1911C-1919C	70.95	94.40	118.00	141.60	165.20
$ 5	1912-1914	72.60	96.80	121.00	145.20	160.40
$10	1912-1914	145.20	193.60	242.00	290.40	338.00
$20	1967	158.70	211.60	264.50	317.40	370.30
$ 5 M.L.	1982-1986	30.00	40.00	50.00	60.00	70.00
$10 M.L.	1982-1986	75.00	100.00	125.00	150.00	175.00
$50 M.L.	1979-1986	300.00	400.00	500.00	600.00	700.00
$100	1976 (Unc.)	75.00	100.00	125.00	150.00	175.00
$100	1976 (Pf)	150.00	200.00	250.00	300.00	350.00
$100	1977-1986	150.00	200.00	250.00	300.00	350.00
$100	1987 (pf)	75.00	100.00	125.00	150.00	175.00

BULLION VALUES OF CANADIAN SILVER COINS

(Computed from $5/troy ounce to $50/troy ounce in increments of $10 Canadian)

Denom.	Fineness	$5	$10	$20	$30	$40	$50
$1	.800	3.00	6.00	12.00	18.00	24.00	30.00
$1	.500	1.88	3.75	7.50	11.25	15.00	18.75
50-cents	.925	1.74	3.47	6.94	10.41	13.88	17.35
50-cents	.800	1.50	3.00	6.00	9.00	12.00	15.00
25-cents	.925	.87	1.73	3.46	5.19	6.92	8.65
25-cents	.800	.75	1.50	3.00	4.50	6.00	7.50
25-cents	.500	.47	.94	1.88	2.82	3.76	4.70
10-cents	.925	.35	.69	1.38	2.07	2.76	3.45
10-cents	.800	.30	.60	1.20	1.80	2.40	3.00
10-cents	.500	.19	.38	.76	1.14	1.52	1.90
5-cents	.925	.17	.34	.68	1.02	1.36	1.70
5-cents	.800	.15	.30	.60	.90	1.20	1.50

OTHER TITLES AVAILABLE FROM THE CHARLTON PRESS

THE CHARLTON STANDARD CATALOGUE OF
CANADIAN COLONIAL TOKENS, FIRST EDITION

The most authoritative reference book ever published on Canadian Colonial Tokens. Each chapter includes detailed information on the history behind the tokens. All provincial, regal, semi-regal and private issues including Wellington and Blacksmith tokens plus the Bouquet Sous of Lower Canada are detailed. The catalogue contains illustrations with complete technical data and full pricing tables. No other book serves as both a reference and pricing guide. This publication provides tables cross-referencing Breton and Corteau numbers with the Charlton numbering system. An ideal catalogue for the collector, dealer and beginner, the Charlton Standard Catalogue of Canadian Colonial Tokens is the best book of its kind on the market.

THE CHARLTON STANDARD CATALOGUE OF
CANADIAN GOVERNMENT PAPER MONEY, SECOND EDITION

This recently released edition covers paper money issued by government authorities from the French Colonial issues to the Bank of Canada issues of 1986. This informative catalogue includes all army bills, provincial issues, Municipal issues, Province of Canada and Dominion of Canada notes. It is more than just a catalogue, with complete technical data tables, full pricing tables, imprints, signatures, anomalies and more, it is an excellent reference book that has proven itself indispensable for both collector and dealer.

THE CHARLTON STANDARD CATALOGUE OF
CANADIAN COINS FORTY SECOND EDITION

The authority in the field of Canadian numismatics. This new edition features over 200 pages filled with updated photographs and complete technical data. Over 8,000 prices in eight different grades from "Good" to "Mint State 65" (collectors' coins to Proof 65) are listed.

The modern collector demands more information from his or her hobby. The 42nd edition of the Charlton Standard Catalogue of Canadian Coins has met this need as the indispensable tool for the numismatic hobbyist. A completely new typestyle has been used throughout for increased legibility in the extensive pricing tables giving the collector a complete reference book and an easy to read pricing authority.

This revised edition offers updated information in all categories from the French Regime to the 1988 Calgary Winter Olympic coins. Including the local pre-decimal coins of Nova Scotia, New Brunswick, Prince Edward Island and Newfoundland. Truly the only catalogue for today's collector of Canadian Coins.

Printed in Canada